3-D CITY GUIDES

AMSTERDAM